CYBER PATROL

Written by

ROBERT CUTTING

Illustrated by

JIM GRAVES

MARK LEWIS

CARI

LUCY LAI

CYBERDOOM

FICTIONAL CHARACTERS

MARK LEWIS: A 12-year-old boy who is an expert at computer games.

CARI: An android who controls Cyber Patrol.

LUCY LAI: The President of Internet Repair Inc. and creator of CyberDoom.

CYBERDOOM: A powerful virus that attacks the Internet.

Contents

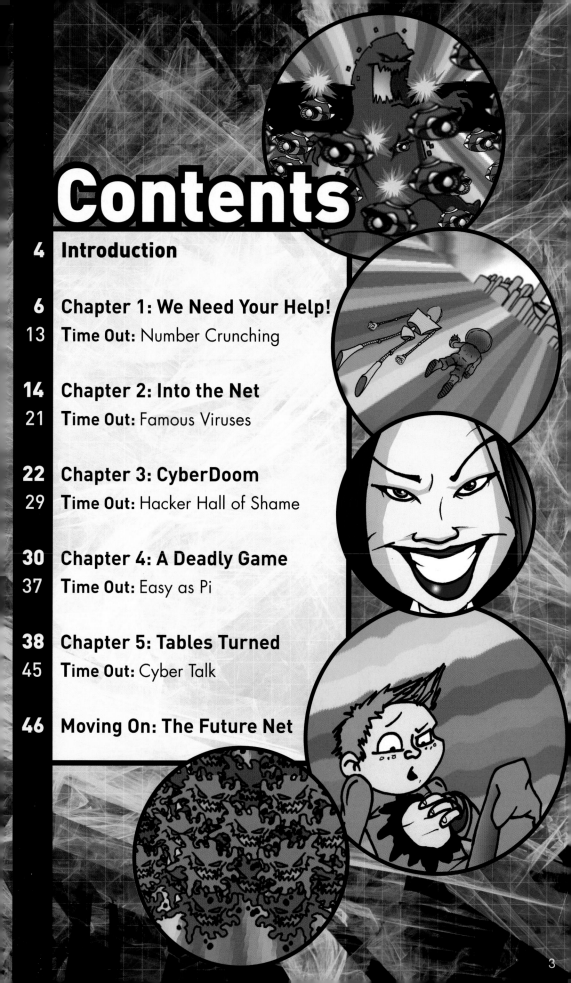

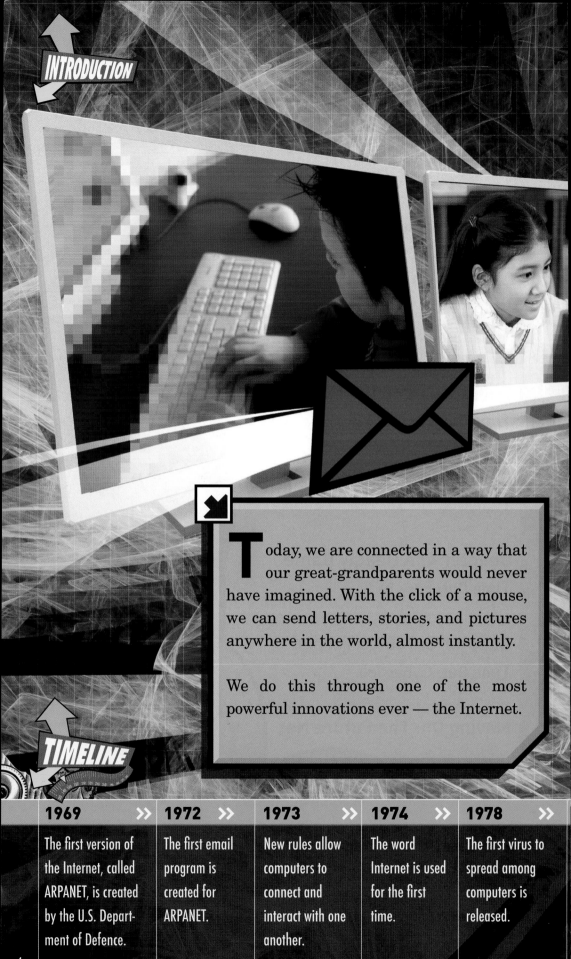

Today, we are connected in a way that our great-grandparents would never have imagined. With the click of a mouse, we can send letters, stories, and pictures anywhere in the world, almost instantly.

We do this through one of the most powerful innovations ever — the Internet.

TIMELINE

1969	1972	1973	1974	1978
The first version of the Internet, called ARPANET, is created by the U.S. Department of Defence.	The first email program is created for ARPANET.	New rules allow computers to connect and interact with one another.	The word Internet is used for the first time.	The first virus to spread among computers is released.

For computer users who play online games, the Internet is more than a place for getting information. It is cyberspace, a virtual world where they can have adventures in 3D.

In the future, a trip into cyberspace could be a reality. But what awaits us there?

WHAT'S THE STORY?

This story is set in an imaginary future. Its characters and events are fictitious.

1983 »»	1990 »»	1993 »»	1996 »»	2006 »»
The Domain Name System is created. Website addresses can now be written as names, not numbers.	Tim Berners-Lee creates the World Wide Web.	The first web browser is created, allowing Internet users to search, retrieve, and display data and documents.	New ideas are introduced for the next generation of the Internet — Internet 2.	There are more than 20 billion web pages, and counting ...

CHAPTER 1: WE NEED YOUR HELP!

IN THE YEAR 2083, THE INTERNET IS IN 3D. PEOPLE NOW USE HOLOGRAPHIC COMPUTERS — HOLOPUTERS!

INTERNET WEBSITES ARE FULLY INTERACTIVE.

ONLINE HOLOPUTER GAMES BECOME MORE POPULAR THAN EVER.

THE INTERNET IS FREE OF VIRUSES AND WORMS ...

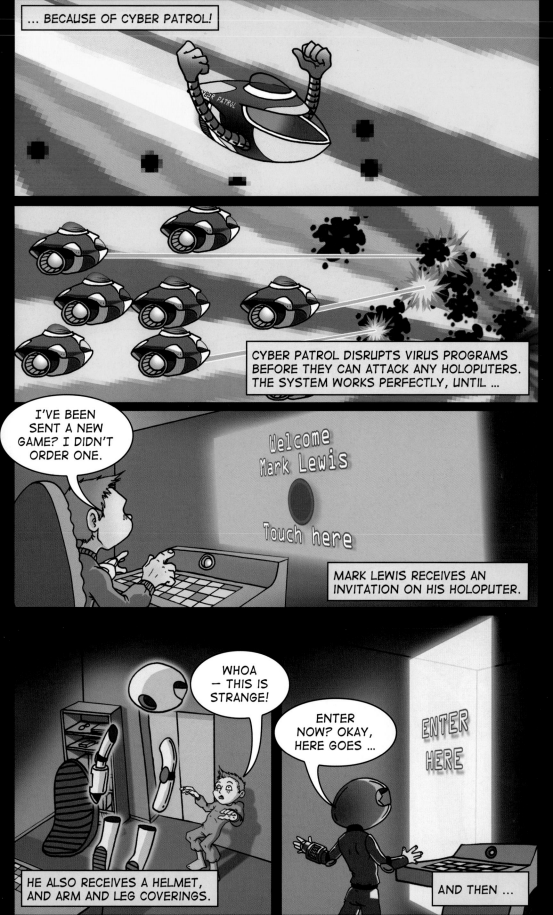

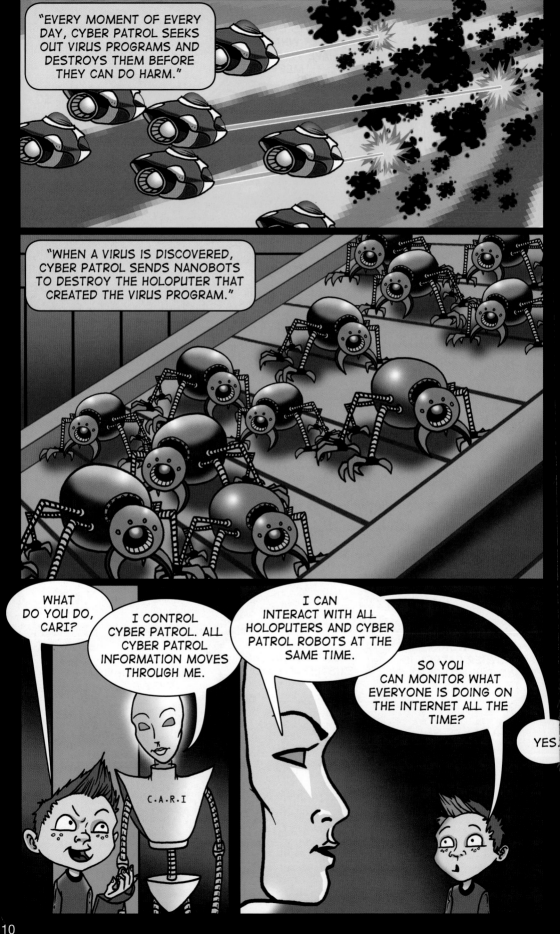

NUMBER CRUNCHING

1 billion — Estimated number of people in the world using the Internet in 2006. The world population at the time was 6.5 billion.

8.5 million — Number of Canadian households with one or more computers as of 2004.

80 000 — Average number of blogs created each day since 2003. Blog is the short form of "web log" and refers to an online journal.

2000 — Number of new lawsuits worldwide against illegal music file sharers.

325 — Number of legal online music sites in the world as of April 2006.

31 — Average number of hours Internet users spent online per month as of March 2006.

CHAPTER 2: INTO THE NET

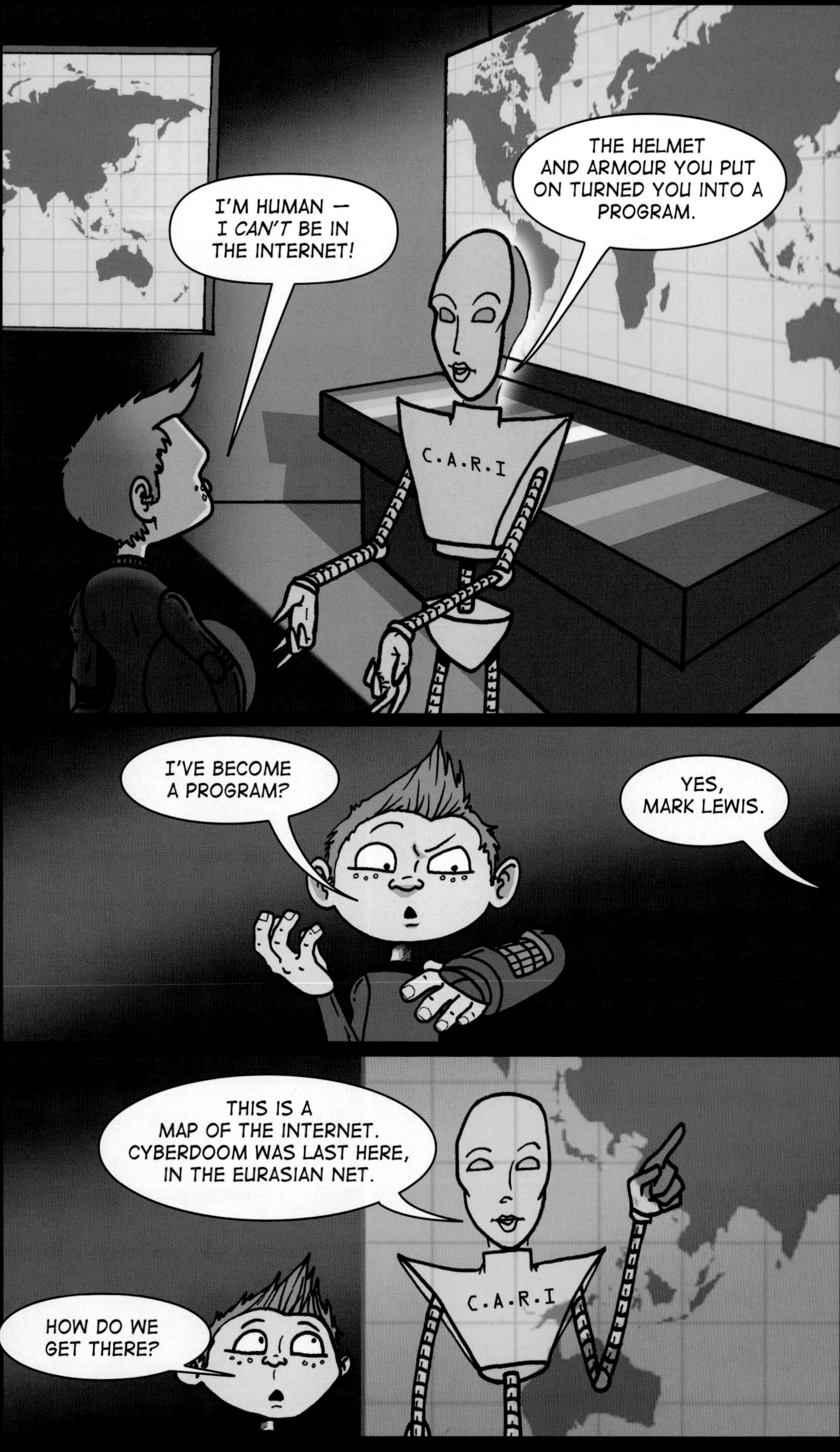

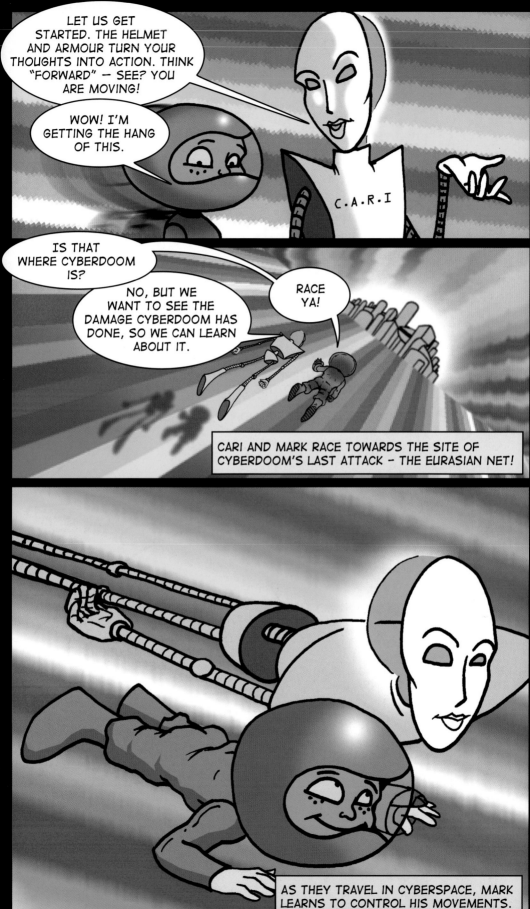

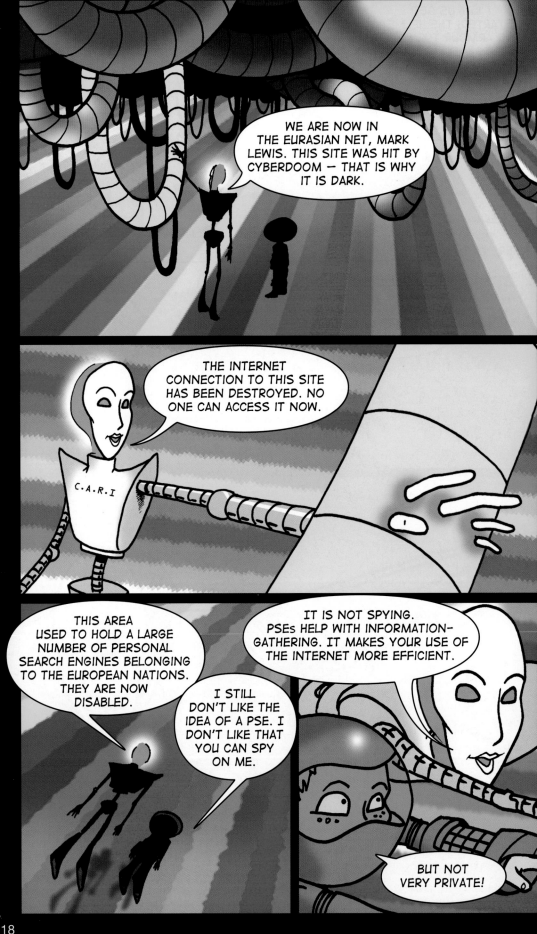

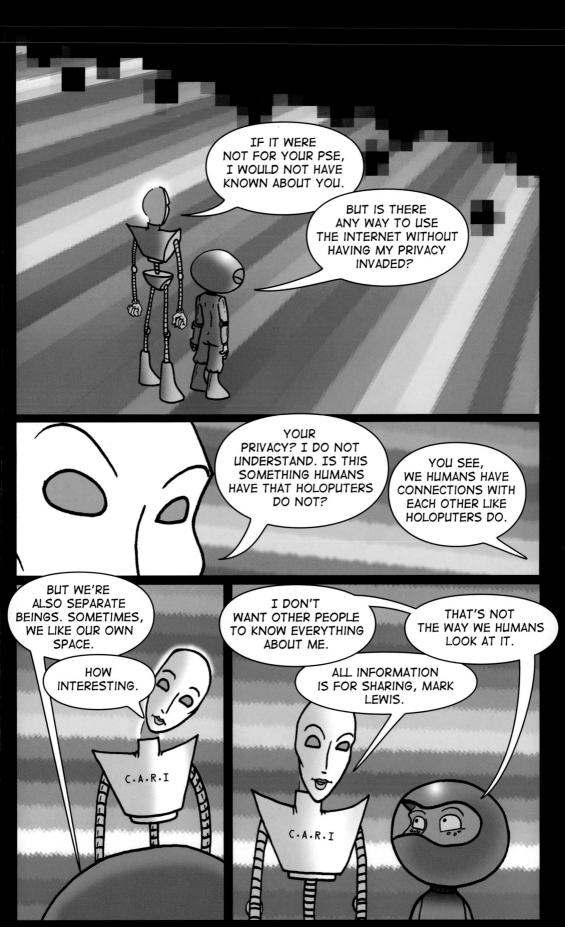

FAMOUS VIRUSES

In medicine, a virus is a kind of germ that spreads disease from person to person. In the computer world, a virus is a program designed to harm computers. Viruses erase or move files on your computer. They can cause your computer to stop working.

1998 The virus "Chernobyl" was discovered. It could use up all the memory on a computer, prevent anti-virus software from running, and even erase a computer's hard drive.

1999 "Melissa" infected more than 100 000 computers over three days. It spread via email.

2000 Like Melissa, the "ILOVEYOU" virus spread via the user's email. It attacked and erased files on a computer's hard drive.

VIRUS ALERT!

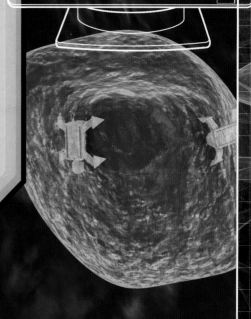

CHAPTER 3: CYBERDOOM

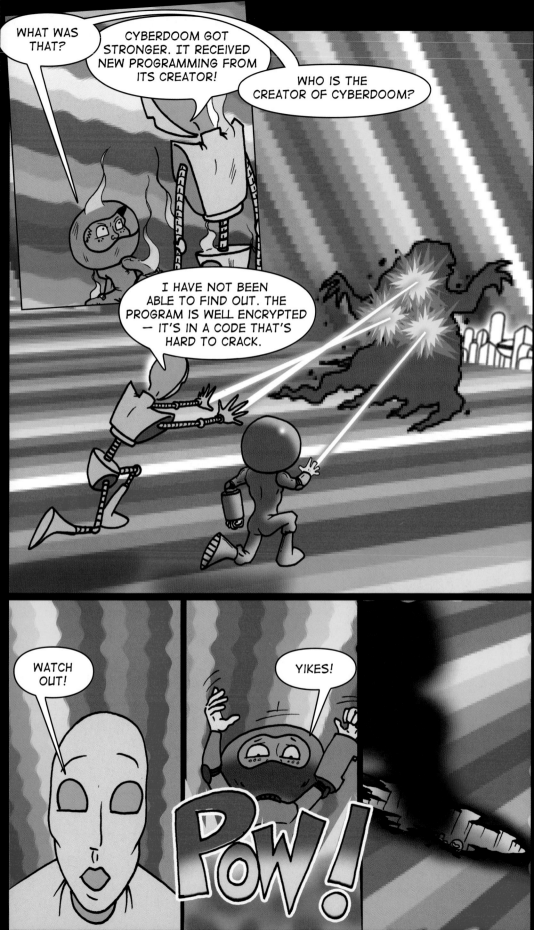

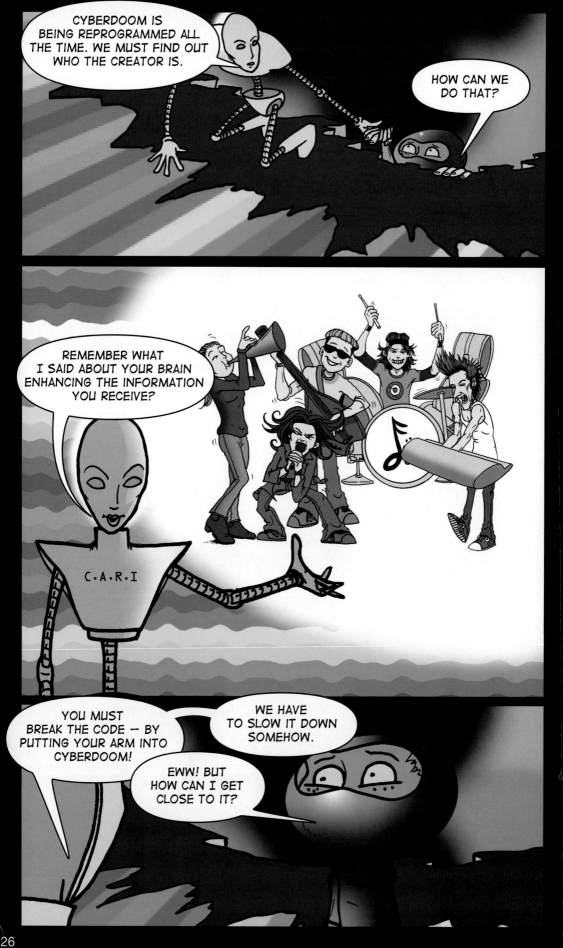

HACKER HALL OF SHAME

Hackers break into personal or business computers to destroy or steal confidential information.

KEVIN POULSEN

In 1990, he took over all the telephone lines of a Los Angeles radio station so that he could win a radio contest for a Porsche. The FBI caught up with him, and in 1994 he was sentenced to 51 months in jail.

VLADIMIR LEVIN

In 1995, he was the mastermind behind a hacker gang that tricked an American bank's computers into spitting out $10 million. He was arrested and spent three years in jail. He was ordered to pay the bank his share from the heist.

MAFIABOY

In 2000, this Canadian teen sent vast amounts of data to the CNN website, causing it to fail. He also hacked other major websites, causing an estimated $1.7 billion U.S. dollars in damages. In 2001, he was sentenced to eight months in a detention centre.

CHAPTER 4: A DEADLY GAME

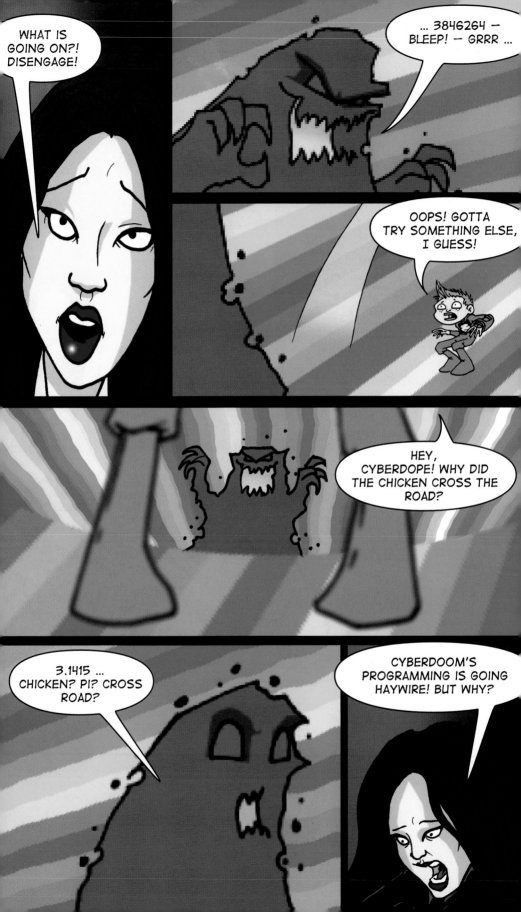

Easy As Pi

In geometry, pi (pronounced PIE) is the ratio of a circle's circumference to its diameter. It is often written as the Greek letter π. Pi is used in math, engineering, and physics.

Pi is often rounded off to 3.14, but it is actually an infinite decimal, meaning that its decimal places have no end. One supercomputer has calculated pi to over one trillion digits, but no one has been able to find an end or pattern to the number.

Many people make a hobby of memorizing as many decimal places of pi as they can. On July 2, 2005, a Japanese man named Akira Haraguchi broke the world record for the most digits of pi ever recited from memory — 83 431!

Here are the first 100 decimal places of pi:
3.14159265358979323846264338327950
28841971693993751058209749445923078116
4062862089986280348253421170679.

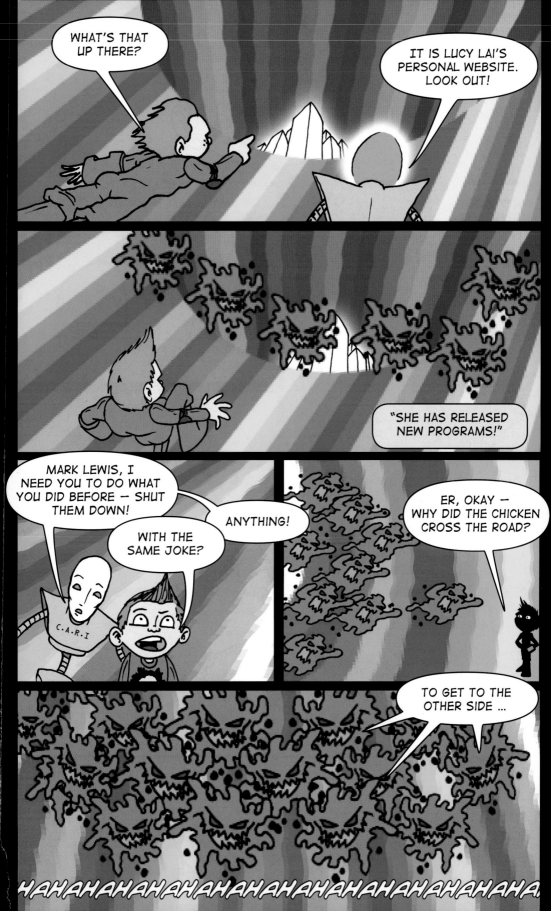

CYBER TALK

Are you familiar with all the words in this list?

ANDROID: a robot that looks human

CYBERSPACE: the world that computer users inhabit when they are online

DISRUPTER: a device that sends out a signal to prevent another signal from working

ENCRYPTED: converted into a secret code to protect information

HOLOGRAM: a three-dimensional image

NANOBOT: a super-tiny robot, about one micrometre in size

PROTOCOL: a code that allows computers to communicate with one another

VIDSTREAM: a video that you can watch on the Internet

WORM: a type of computer virus that doesn't attach itself to a specific program

What other words can you add to the list to show you are Internet-savvy?

THE FUTURE

Before 1991, only computer scientists and military personnel used the Internet. Today, almost a billion people around the world use the Internet to work, study, and do everything from downloading music to watching baby eagles hatch on the other side of the world!

The new version of the Internet — Internet 2 — allows for greater high-speed transfer of data. Experts think it will change our lives just as much as the first Internet has.

NET

Here are a few predictions about how the Internet might work in the future. Which ones are more likely to happen soon?

- Doctors will perform surgery on astronauts in outer space, using cyber scalpels and 3D imaging.
- We will exercise by playing sports online with our favourite professional teams.
- We will use the Internet with our eyeglasses.
- We will transport ourselves around the world without getting on an airplane.

Responsible Internet use is important. So is awareness of privacy and safety.

- Do not give out personal information to strangers.
- Be careful when you are making new friends on the Internet.
- Double-check information from websites for its accuracy.
- Don't open email from people you don't know.
- Stay away from websites or chat rooms that are unsuitable for kids.

INDEX